I HAVE A DREAM

I HAVE A DREAM

Irish Children Writing
for RTÉ's *Millennium Eve*

Published in 1999 in association with RTÉ
by Marino Books
an imprint of Mercier Press
16 Hume Street Dublin 2
Tel: (01) 661 5299; Fax: (01) 661 8583
E-mail: books@marino.ie

Trade enquiries to CMD Distribution
55A Spruce Avenue
Stillorgan Industrial Park
Blackrock County Dublin
Tel: (01) 294 2556; Fax: (01) 294 2564
E-mail: cmd@columba.ie

ISBN 1 86023 106 3

10 9 8 7 6 5 4 3 2 1

A CIP record for this title is available from the British Library

Cover design by Penhouse Design
Typeset by Deirdre's Desktop
Printed in Ireland by ColourBooks, Baldoyle Industrial Estate, Dublin 13

FOREWORD

The end of the millennium gives us a unique opportunity to celebrate the cultural heritage of the last millennium and to look forward to a new century. At this important time RTÉ hopes to highlight the arts in Ireland, and we rejoice in our artistic achievements in a range of areas. We wish to focus on the future of the arts in this country and believe that it is vital to foster and encourage young creative talent.

With this in mind, RTÉ is delighted to present this very special book which documents the dreams and hopes of Irish children from all over the country. On the following pages there are tales of trees with Maltesers, dinosaur days, worlds where animals rule, dreams of peace and happiness, hopes of reconciliation and love.

We are thrilled to have initiated this project for Irish writing talent and would like to thank all those who entered the very special *I Have a Dream* competition. RTÉ would like to thank Breige Galligan, Micheál Dineen, Don Conroy, Clare Ranson, Berndadette McHugh, Shaun Byrne, Gene Mehigan, Peggy Cruickshank, Bill Wall and Gabriel Fitzmaurice – our panel of judges – who did great work in making the selection of poems and stories for the book. Our sincere gratitude to the team at Mercier Press/Marino Books for publishing this book. Finally, a very special thank you to poet John Agard from whose original idea this *I Have a Dream* project was developed.

We are delighted to introduce the new Irish writers of the next millennium.

JOE MULHOLLAND, MANAGING DIRECTOR
RTÉ TELEVISION

INTRODUCTION

On the eve of a new millennium, as a new curriculum is introduced into our primary schools, the schoolboys and schoolgirls of the new Ireland describe their dreams. It goes to prove that the more things change, the more they remain the same. Our children articulate the timeless concerns not just of childhood, but of all humankind. If Utopia is no longer a viable dream, then a world of love and peace and justice is still a realistic aspiration; a world where people live in harmony with one another and with their environment; a world where humans respect themselves and their fellow creatures on this sacred earth.

The world of the imagination is no less important. Time and again, children enter a world that transcends the tyranny of logic, where the mind can float freely and make marvellous and playful connections. This is, to paraphrase the poet Patrick Kavanagh, 'An unworn world made of green things and blue things and arguments that cannot be proven'. In this book we have a fine representation of the children of this country. Facing into a new millennium, they are not paralysed by fear; rather they look into the future full of joyful hope.

GABRIEL FITZMAURICE

KEITH MCLOUGHLIN, ST JOHN'S NS,

BALLYSADARE, COUNTY SLIGO

I would play in Croke Park handball alley, in the All Ireland 60x30 final. The winner would be the ultimate player. He would be No 1 unless he was beaten. I am a journalist for the *Irish Independent* for GAA, but today is my day off. The man I am playing is from the county of Kilkenny. I am pleased to take after my father and great-grandfather, though the sport has risen in popularity. In the game I wear the black-and-white shirt and step into my position, and with one massive strike at the ball I rattle the court and start the final. I make desperate attempts to hit more hard balls and succeed. We are both sweating and our fists are black with bruises. It's a last game, one strike could win it. Then I hit that ball and kill it! I am the first Sligo man to win. I am only twenty-one, the new kid, and then I bring the trophy home, and the song 'the Isles of Innisfree' rings in my ears. I have a dream.

KILIAN PATRICK O'SULLIVAN, DIVINE WORD NS,
MARLEY GRANGE, DUBLIN

I have a dream,
It is a vision,
I see trees, castles and blue skies,
The fields and hills are green.

There is no rubbish, no pollution,
The fish are jumping in the streams,
I am having a picnic,
Laughing and happy.

The wars are over,
There is peace in the North.
When we go home, I can sleep
And have more dreams.

I wish that when I die I could see my Grandad up in heaven and see all my dead cats. I could see Enid Blyton too. I love her books. It would be fun to see my Grandad again.

I have a dream that I could help the poor people.

I have a dream that I am a famous ballerina.

I have a dream that I am a famous singer, and I wish I was a queen.

Tá taibhreamh agam go mbead i mo thréidlia (vet) lá éigin. Is breá liom ainmhithe, go mór-mhór cait agus madraí. Tá a lán ainmhithe agam sa bhaile. Tá dhá chat agam agus dhá phiscín agus madra beag. Samhradh is ainm di.

Bím ag taibhreamh mar gheall ar gach aon rud. Bím ag taibhreamh go bhfuilim pósta agus cúpla leanbh agam agus bíonn saol aoibhinn agam ag obair mar thréidlia. Lá amháin sa taibhreamh tagann madra isteach lena mháistir. Tá cairt taréis é a bhualadh.

Cuirfead an madra suas ar bhórd speisialta agus tosnód á shaoradh. Beidh an madra gortaithe go dona. Cuirfead a lán greamanna ar a dhroim ach fós ní bheidh feabhas air. Taréis cúpla uair a chloig geobhad amach go mbeidh sé marbh. Bead díreach ag an ndoras nuair a chloisfead cúpla scread. Rithfead go dtí an mbord. Geobhad amach gur ina chodladh a bhí sé nuair a bhíos ag tabhairt na greamanna dó. Bead chomh sásta liom féin. Bhraihfead go h-iontach ar fad. Beidh a mhaístir ana-shásta liom. Tabharfaidh sé a lán airgid dom.

Beidh clú agus cáil orm mar thréidlia ar fud na tíre. Bead ag sábháil ainmhithe bochta ar feadh mo shaoil. Ainmhithe a thagann amach san oíche cosúil leis an mbroc bocht agus an madra rua glic. Ainmhithe a mhaireann ar an bhfeirm – an bhó bhreac agus a gamhain. Agus peataí le leanaí agus gan dabht mo Shamhradh beag féin. Mo mhadra beag aoibhinn.
Sin é mo thaibhreamh.
Ba bhreá liom a bheith i mo thréidlia.

Ailbhe Hogan, Barefield NS, Ennis, Co Clare

CLAIRE DONNELLY (8), MOYGLASS NS, KYLEBRACK, LOUGHREA, COUNTY GALWAY

Bell of Freedom

I have a dream of a silent bell
That rings in the heart of a slave
As he trudges his way on life's weary path
While freedom awaits him in his grave.

So ring, little bell, let your sound be heard,
Bring joy to the lonely and weak,
And I hope some day in God's own way
We can all live the life that we seek.

MARY GLEESON (9), CLYDAGH NS, HEADFORD, COUNTY GALWAY

I have a dream that the world would be perfect, politicians would be decent people, and death, injury, sickness and war would not exist. Oops! I left out a bit – my little brother wouldn't be so annoying! But then again, some things I can't do in the future, but I will do them now. If a child's world were perfect, cartoons would be the only thing on TV, CD players would be

20p and sweets would be exceptionally nutritious. But when I dream, I dream of more simple things. Such as going to all-night parties, fat-free chocolate and nice clothes.

But – yes, there's a 'but' in it – some things we've go to do, whether we like them or not, like eating sprouts, doing homework, tidying your room and wearing stupid clothes (although they're not stupid in your parents' opinion). My dream is really about people being nicer, i.e. not gossiping about your friends, ruining public property or writing on desks in the library. So, people could be a lot nicer if they just had some respect. So there you have it, that's my dream. If it sounded complicated just read it again . . . what are you waiting for, read it again! Fine, if you're not going to read it again, I may as well carry on. Say, did you ever see that *Carry On* movie where . . . Oh, never mind, you're not interested. Now, apart from having a dream, I have a nightmare that a war will start in the Republic. I know there's a 'war' in the North right now, but one in the Republic would be much worse. So we've got to prevent them. So my dream is really about the world being a better place for generations to come. Oh yeah, and please don't write on desks in the library.

I have a dream
Of mystic lands,
Of dancing fairies
Hand in hand,
Of brave knights
And their gallant deeds,
Of unicorns, pegasi,
And noble steeds.

I have a dream
Of snow-white birds
With golden elegant wings
Which soar over mountains
And oceans,
Where a beautiful mermaid sings.

I have a dream
of crystal-clear ponds
Where the toad and the otter play,
Of dense and dark woodlands
Where the otter sings all day.

I have a dream
Of rocky mountains
And cool fresh mountain streams.
What a pity, what a shame
That these are only dreams.

AMY DUNNE, BARNASHRONE NS,
MOUNTMELLICK, COUNTY LAOIS

I have a dream that my family would be allowed to keep my baby sister and adopt her and she would be a part of my family and grow up with me. Her name is Michaela and we have her now for a year.

LAUREN CAMPBELL (7), ST JOSEPH'S GIRLS' NS,
KINGSCOURT, COUNTY CAVAN

I have a dream
To be a vet,
To help animals, because
I love pets.

I have a dream
To be a queen
And make a law that everyone
Must sing.
I have a dream
To be rich and famous,
To travel the world
To meet lots of people with
Interesting faces.
It would be lovely to be
Rich and famous.

I have a dream
To be on *Den 2*,
To play with Dustin
And be on TV too.

I wish you had these dreams too.

ANITA QUINN, DROMORE NS, KILLYGORDON, CO DONEGAL

I have a dream that I could prevent the savage oppression that people suffered back in the unforgettable times of the bitterly resented workhouse from ever happening. It was to my utter consternation to hear of the dreadful poverty which people lived in in the time of the Great Famine.

Gaunt and weary bodies worked ceaselessly as they retaliated against the dreadful atmosphere of the workhouse. Many of the misfortunate victims of the workhouse had dubious pasts and were without family. People were sentenced to the workhouse through no fault of their own. A mixture of fungi and other substances travelled from South America to Ireland, which caused a blight to break out on Irish potatoes. Many Irish citizens depended on potatoes to survive, and this caused the Great Famine to arise.

Workhouses were set up in different parts of Ireland, catering for the sick and homeless affected by the Great Famine. The workhouse was a greatly detested place and people hated the thought of staying there. Men and women were separated in the workhouse, so many families were split up. Disease and germs wafted through the workhouse, giving many people little chance of survival.

The indifferent workhouse wardens were oblivious to the perfidious act they were committing. They were detached and uninterested in the condition of the victims' bodies. Workhouse victims' bodies were a bilious green from the disease circulating there. The victims worked ceaselessly and were quite listless from working.

Isolated and tremulous workhouse children cried copiously as they were being separated from family and friends. Victims lived a hand-to-mouth existence and felt bitter resentment towards the hostile workhouse wardens. They worked industriously and received a paltry reward for their slavery.

I felt great sympathy towards these people. I have a dream to turn back time. I would get to the root of the problem which caused the fungus to infest Irish potatoes and how it caused the blight. If I was able to warn people about the blight before it came, then workhouses would not have been erected and people would not have been sentenced to slavery for the rest of their lives.

Spare a thought for those affected by the workhouse. Some of them died a bitter death and others had only a happy loving memory of their loved ones, whom they missed so much.

SHAUNA O'GORMAN (5), BEALAD NS,
CLONAKILTY, COUNTY CORK

I have a dream of being a pop star.
It was lovely. I was all dressed up
And there was a big audience watching me.
I was the lead singer in a band.
Everyone was having a great time
Waving their hands in the air
And singing along with me.
All my family were up at the front
And looked very proud of me.
My younger sister sang one song with me.
The name of the song was 'She's My Sister'.
I love my sister.
I hope some day my dream will come true
And maybe some of my friends will join the band
with me.
We can call it 'Shauna's Little Dream'.

GERARDA HAWKES (12), GURRANE NS,
INNISHANNON, COUNTY CORK

I have a dream
That the sad would not be sad
That the sick would not be sick
That the poor would not be poor
And that the bad would not be bad.

I'd like Northern Ireland to be peaceful and quiet
And not have all those killings, bombs and lots of
riots.

I'd like the world to see
What a lovely place it could be,
'Cause if more people dreamed like me
Oh what a lovely place it could be.

CLARE HICKEY (7), DUBLIN

I have a dream of a faraway place
That's higher than the clouds and higher than space.

I have a horse there that's very short.
I also have my own tennis court.

23

I eat cake and ice cream every day,
And there are bright colours – not black, brown or
grey.

I have lots of toys and lots of fun,
And I always play with everyone.

I hope you will love it, because I do.
It's a wonderful land, where dreams come true.

JACQUELINE O'NEILL (10), INCHICORE GIRLS' NS, DUBLIN

I have a dream about being part of a real family.

I am not part of a family. I mean a real family. I just have a mammy and brothers and sisters. You might think that that is a family but it is not. A real family is a mammy and a daddy and brothers and sisters.

My dream is to have my daddy back. I have not seen my daddy for three years. Soon it will be four years. My dream is to belong to a real family and have my daddy back again.

RUTH MOONEY (7), ST BRIGID'S SCHOOL,
BALLSBRIDGE, DUBLIN

I have a dream to be a writer
And write mysterious tales,
With lots of ghosts and witches,
Where the monster always fails.

I have a dream to be a writer
To make my fortune and fame.
I would travel to Pompeii
And the world would know my name.

I have a dream to be a writer,
And like J. K. Rowling I would be.
She wrote my favourite books,
Which really inspired me.

LISA O'REILLY (11), ST MARY'S NS, DRUNG, CAVAN

I have a dream. I hope that one day there will be peace
in our country and throughout the world. I admire
people like Mo Mowlam and John Hume and David
Trimble who try to bring people together to bring
about peace. It is my ambition one day to be able to
bring about peace.

I agree with those politicians who believe that talking to each other can bring about peace. Even those people who are terrorists need to be listened to and maybe this will help to stop the fighting. I especially admire Mo Mowlam, who has been criticised in the past for talking to these people, but she still carries on doing her best to get peace.

It's not just our own country that needs peace. Countries throughout the world are at war and they need people who are willing to work on their behalf by bringing in food and supplies and in some cases urging governments to take refugees. I would like to see richer countries accept more of these people and do more to help them.

If one day I found myself in a position to do so, I would ban all nuclear bombs and the type of weapons that were used in the Gulf War. Many countries throughout the world have enough bombs and weapons to kill millions of people. If governments joined together to stop the making of these, the world would be a better place. Hopefully in my lifetime countries like Ireland and Iraq will find peace that will last for future generations.

LAURA FLYNN, RATHGORMACK NS, CARRICK-ON-SUIR, CO WATERFORD

Sunny days and ice cream,
Being on the winning team,
Fun and laughter as we scream.

We think about the millennium,
We call it my little lemon mum
To remember it.
We would like it to be just like this year,
Ooops! It's getting very near.

At the moment this is what we do,
Maybe it's really not so new:
At school
We play
Everyday,
We run
In the sun,
We have fun,
We get lots of work done.

In every class
We learn new things:
Why do birds have wings?

We get very smart indeed
As we learn to read.
It really is a glorious sight
As we learn to write.
We don't just sit on our bums.
Excuse me! We're doing sums.

What makes the earth quake?
Why is the daddy duck a drake?
Which is the nearest planet?
Is there a rock harder than granite?

There are lots of children here,
They are all very dear.
Some are neat,
Most are sweet,
Some are small,
Some are tall,
But there is only one of each –
All the easier to teach.

It's just afternoon,
How did it come so soon?
Tummies rumble,
Little people get hungry
And start to dream of apple crumble.
We eat lunch –

Munch, munch, crunch, crunch –
Oh me oh my, I have a hunch
That we are a happy bunch.

After class
We play in the grass,
We catch the ball
We bounce it against the wall,
We learn to share and pass,
We try to never break the glass.

We play hide and seek,
Some people hide,
Some people seek,
Some creep,
Some leap,
Some peep,
Some almost fall asleep,
Some pretend that they are sheep,
Some make noises like a jeep.

Sometimes things get lost,
Sometimes they get found
On the ground,
All around,
Like Áine's glasses on the wall –
Luckily they didn't fall.

Shhh! I hear the bell,
Now I know that all is well.
It is time to go home,
And that is the end of our poem.

Except to say before we go
That on January 1st we will know
Was it really worth the fuss and cheer
Or was it just another New Year?
Either way
First class at Abbeycartron
Want to say,
'Welcome My Little Lemon Mum –
The millennium.'

NIAMH HORSCROFT (7), ST MARY'S PRIMARY SCHOOL,
CUSHENDALL, COUNTY ANTRIM

I have a dream that I could live in a sweet land. I would
eat all the sweets I could. The grass would be made of
rice-paper and the leaves of trees would be made of
jelly-bears. Chimney pots would be lollipops and front
doors would be massive bars of chocolate. Ponds and
lakes would be made of melted chocolate and walking
sticks would be those funny walking-stick candy
things. Flowerpots would be rice-paper bun cases and

have buns for soil. Slates for the roofs would be square-shaped bits of chocolate. Even clothes would be made of rice-paper.

CONN MACGIB (11), SCOIL AN TSEACHTAR LAOCH, BAILE MUNNA, BAILE ÁTHA CLIATH

I have a dream almost every night –
But it's not very pleasant, it gives me quite a fright –
About a whole new world where the animal rules
And treats us humans like servants and fools.
The dog keeps us outside when it's wet,
The fish they fry us when they catch us in a net.
The pigs they fatten us up for the kill,
The horses makes us pull heavy carts up the hill.
The monkeys they lock us up in large cages,
They laugh and throw food, they think it's
outrageous.
But the worst one of all is the cheetah, he's rude,
He skins us right down till we're left in the nude.
So next time you're with an animal, don't be bold
Because you never know what the future may hold.

I have a dream, it's rather queer,
That things will start to change next year.
My life will change a lot as well;
Of my dreams I will now tell.
The environment will be much cleaner
And everyone will be a lot keener
To keep it clean when they see
How beautiful our world could be.

Jeans and combats will be out,
And tracksuits too, without a doubt.
Galactic materials will be in,
And all the rest will go in the bin.

Robots will work in factories
And sweets will grow on all the trees.
Carlow will win the Sam Maguire
And there will be no famine or fire.

The world will be peaceful all over again
And there won't be any wars between men.
Anyone could land on Mars
And we won't need petrol for our cars.

Now all my dreams have been told to you
And hopefully they will come true
Soon the third millennium will be here at last
And worry and war will be a thing of the past.

RACHEL MCHUGH (7), DRUMNABEY PRIMARY SCHOOL,
CASTLEDERG, COUNTY TYRONE

I have a dream that there will be no more wars, no more earthquakes, no more tornadoes. Everyone will live longer and have happy lives. People will be peaceful and contented. I have a dream that there will be no more fighting in the world, especially in Northern Ireland, where I live. My very special dream is that cures may be found for bad diseases and especially for cystic fibrosis, so that I do not have to do physio every day.

MICHELLE NAUGHTON (12), GORTJORDAN NS,
KILMAINE, COUNTY MAYO

I have a dream where the skies are always blue
The sun is always shining
And every flower blooms.

Kids are always playing
Laughter fills the air
You can do almost anything
To this place none can compare.

Maybe this is heaven
It could even be on earth
Let's all wish for the best for this millennium rebirth.

COLLEEN MURRAY (7), HOLY CROSS SCHOOL,
DUNDRUM, DUBLIN

I have a dream of peaceful lives
Without any bombs, guns or knives,
That all people could come together
To love and care for each other.
If I could dream a dream tonight,
I would dream that everything would be all right.

Vanessa Newman, Scoil Bríde, Leixlip, Co Kildare

MARIE SALEH (12), ST JOHN'S NS, BREAFFY,
CASTLEBAR, COUNTY MAYO

I have many dreams, some deep, some frivolous (normally about a Lotto win!), some almost nightmarish (normally about my sister!).

But this dream is futuristic, optimistic . . .

In my dream mankind's memories of continuous suffering and excruciating pain have been eradicated, eliminated, replaced. Earth's inhabitants have been set free from the claws of fear, hatred, racism and bigotry.

Courageous men and women who willingly and non-violently have sacrificed life itself in an attempt for peace and equality see their sacrifices being rewarded in the new millennium. The imprisonment of one's generous, sharing spirit within one's own materialistic body is now a thing of the past!

Corrupt and violent nationalistic ways have joined the deceased. Truly there falls a cloak of peace and tranquillity upon the earth. Cruel diseases that once savagely roamed the earth seeking to devour both young and old are wiped out completely.

Dark alleys, once havens for drug dealers and mobs of hostile gangsters, have been cleansed of such loathsome characters.

Negligent, self-centred politicians have been removed from their elevated positions, to be replaced by those who rule with compassion and deep respect for human life.

The slate of mankind, that once recorded ruthless wars and countless sins, now lies purified of all atrocities. May this ocean of blessings and accomplishments not be transient but continue millennium after millennium to infinity.

I have a dream
The earth is green,
The stars are made of bananas
And the moon wears pyjamas.

I have a dream
When I'm in bed,
The bed is blue and red,
Colours dancing in my head,

A rainbow over my room,
Orange, purple and blue,
Yellow and green,
The nicest colours I've ever seen.

When I wake up the colours are gone,
I still remember what went on.

RORY GILDEA (11), SCOIL MHUIRE,
GLENTIES, COUNTY DONEGAL

I have a dream!
About playing a gig in front
of 50,000 people.
I have a dream
of the exhilaration, the talent of being able
to fire my fingers on the frets of my guitar in
Slane Castle!
The dream of mobs of people cheering,
Screaming, clapping!
Oh, what a dream!

Multi-coloured lights peering down on all of the
band,
The drummer slapping the drum skins like a mother
Breaking out her rage on her child who just broke her
favourite vase!
Guards trying to stop the crowds from coming onto
the stage!
Sweat pouring down my face,
The thought of making a mistake!

I have a dream of being able to create more bands,
where instruments are played instead of those
annoying computer sounds!

I have a dream . . . Oh yes,
A dream!

NORITA CASHMAN (6), CLONKEEN NS,
KILLARNEY, COUNTY KERRY

I have a dream of growing up tall,
As now I am a wee bit small,
Of leaving school and getting a job
Instead of watching *Baby Bob*.
I'd like to teach, like Mrs White,
Little children to read and write.

PUPILS OF THIRD TO SIXTH CLASSES, ARDVARNEY NS,
DROMAHAIR, COUNTY LEITRIM

As the third millennium draws near,
My dreams I set before you here.

I have a dream to play my part
And make next year a brand new start.

I have a dream that all mankind
Will leave its harmful ways behind.

I have a dream that all earth's lands
Will end their wars and join their hands.

I have a dream that black and white
Can live together and end their fight.

I have a dream that we will see
An end to hunger and misery.

I have a dream that the world will be
A cleaner place for you and me.

I have a dream that expertise
Will halt the spread of world disease.

I have a dream that in my time
We will see an end to crime.

I have a dream, to share what I've got
With those around me who haven't a lot.

These are my dreams, I hope that you
Will help me make my dreams come true.

EDEL BROWN (9), ST JOSEPH'S PRIMARY SCHOOL,
GARVAGH, COUNTY DERRY

I have a dream, a lovely dream that I really hope will come true. When I do things during the day I keep thinking about it. Even when I'm trying to get to sleep I think about it. I have got really interested in keeping my dream in my mind. Even when I am reading my magazine I go to the two pages about puppy care and I dream again.

That's right! I'm hoping to get a puppy for Christmas. To be precise, a short-legged Jack Russell. Granny has a little dog like this and I am always eager to visit Granny's house to see her and the dog.

A dog needs care and attention. That's what I have been thinking about very carefully. When everyone is away to school or work a dog needs to be tied up or else it might run away. That is the principal problem that my family has about getting a dog. Also we would need proper facilities such as a kennel or bed.

A dog or puppy is a big responsibility. You need time for a dog, to clean, feed and exercise it and shut it in its kennel or house at night. I have been thinking about that too, and Clare, my sister, and I believe we could keep up and cope with this responsibility but I'm beginning now to think doubtfully.

The thing that caught me in the net of getting a puppy was Granny having one and it doing a lot of amusing things. It pulls at your laces and makes them go out. Granny got a chain lead for the puppy because it would have chewed a rope lead. Even with the chain lead the dog just carries it in its mouth. Granny's dog climbs on her chair and lies round her neck where he tries to get to sleep. It seems to have a bond with the horse because the horse keeps licking it.

My uncle Brendan has a huge dog, and Nell, granny's dog, will not leave Brendan's dog, Cladagh, alone.

A dog can sometimes be a nuisance, especially a puppy that will hide things in the hay, anything like socks or slippers anywhere. You might never see the thing you've lost again. I've taken special note of this but I still want a dog and I don't think anybody or anything can change my mind. For example, if someone told me I could meet a really famous person or have a dog, I would choose the dog.

That's how much I want a dog and I just can't stop fantasising about it. I have a dream that one day soon I'll have a dog.

SUSAN SANTRY (10), SCOIL BARRA CAILINÍ,
BEAUMONT, CORK

Will I be a space traveller
And travel up to space?
Or will I be a runner
And win every single race?
I dreamt I'd be a mermaid
And own the seven seas.
Or I'd like to be a poet,
'To be or not to be'.
I thought I'd be a seamstress,
Make dresses that are divine.

Or will I end up in France,
Squashing grapes for wine?
Maybe I'd be an inventor
Or a crazy scientist.
Or an exterminator,
And get rid of horrible pests.

No one knows what they'll be,
Everyone changes their mind.
Me, I wanted to be a nurse
Or someone else who's kind.
Maybe I'll be a tourist,
Eiffel Tower, here I come!
Or should I be a chocolate-taster,
Yum! Yum! Yum!

After going through these suggestions,
I finally made a decision,
What I think I'm going to be is . . .
a mathematician.

PATRICK HIGGINS (9), KILLASORA NS,
GRANARD, COUNTY LONGFORD

I have a dream to become an astronaut, to walk on the
moon
and Jupiter too.

I have a dream to become a pop star with a number
one tune,
And not in my room.

I have a dream to become a builder and build a house
Or two, and a mansion of course.

I have a dream to become a football star to play on the
field –
And not on the tar – with my hero Michael Owen.

I have a dream to become a policeman, to fight
burglars,
To fight crime and to protect my county, Longford.

I have a dream to become a photographer and travel
the world,
To take pictures of ancient Greece – and of Ireland, of
course.

I have a dream to be just like my Daddy.

LAURA MCBRIDE, ST BRIDGET'S NS, CONVOY, CO DONEGAL

I have a dream. It is January 2009. Everything has changed. Best of all, school has changed. We will go to school at weekends only. There are no more books. Everyone has a computer on their desk. It is hard to get used to typing instead of writing, but if you make a mistake it is easy to change it.

We have only one break. It is fifteen minutes long. I wish we could go back to the way school used to be.

Life is very different. It is topsy-turvy land. Kings live in cottages, beggars in palaces. Houses are triangular. Our bedrooms are downstairs and the kitchen is above. The teacher's desk is at the back of the room. The blackboard is on the ceiling. The teacher has a long stick with a tiny piece of chalk on the top.

Now I think I have told you how my dream life is different.

AMYLEIGH HAND, ST ANNE'S NS, ARDCLOC,
STRAFFAN, COUNTY KILDARE

I have a dream inside my head,
It comes to me when I'm in bed.

I dream of tigers and far-off lands
And wish I could visit the desert sands.

For safari is my dream,
As far away as it may seem.

Rhinos, elephants and monkeys too –
It's so much better than the zoo.

I dream safari all night long
And hear the wild birds sing their song.

I see sun rise and see sun set,
I watch alligators getting wet.

Safari is where I want to be,
It's where I am in my dream, you see.

With all the animals of the wild,
It's my dream, the dream of a child.

So when I close my eyes to sleep,
Pray to God my dream to keep.

I have a dream to captain the Clare senior camogie team to victory in the All Ireland final. If I were fortunate enough to have this amazing dream come true, this is how I would like it to happen.

It was extremely tense on the bus journey up. The bus was as quiet as a grave. Everyone was concentrating on their own game. Each of them knew what they must do. The substitutes tried desperately to break the silence by cracking jokes but failed miserably.

'Now I know what the 1995 Clare senior hurling team must have felt,' I said to myself with a fluttering stomach. I took a picture of them out of my bag. 'I'm going to win it for them,' I said to myself. Those skilful players brought us all such enjoyment watching them play and introduced the game of hurling into my life.

As we sprinted onto the pitch a deafening cheer went up. I looked around – a sea of saffron and blue descended on the hallowed turf of Croke Park.

The referee threw in the sliotar and the game began. We opened the scoring when our centre-back Mary Callinan pointed from a long-range free. Within a minute Galway's midfielder pointed to tie up matters. After this we lost our way somewhat as Galway got on top and scored three points without reply. We ended sixteen minutes without a score when Patrice McNamara scored a twenty-five-metre free, five minutes from half-time. We finished the half strongly when Patrice McNamara and I added four points to the scoreboard.

Galway came out determined after half-time. Their greatly deserved breakthrough came in the sixth minute when their wing-forward got inside the defence and found the net. Four superb Galway points followed and we really could not find any answer to the skilful Galway team. We began to lie down as Galway repeatedly beat us back with clearances from the Galway full-backs. Suddenly I realised the Clare hurling team wouldn't give up. 'In the 1997 All Ireland they came from six points down to win so we surely can come back from four points down,' I said to myself.

I started urging my team on. All of a sudden there was a new spirit in our team. Points were exchanged twice in ten minutes. At last my chance came. Orla O'Connor stormed down the left flank, delivered a great pass to me and I buried it in the back of the net. My goal cut Galway's lead to the minimum and soon the lead was wiped out completely when Patrice pointed from a twenty-metre free. There was a new fire in our play and whatever Galway did they couldn't put that fire out. Three points from Orla and me saw us stretch our lead to three points.

My second goal, two minutes from full-time, from Orla's line ball, was the icing on the cake and confirmed the result, and it was time for the celebrations to begin.

As I lifted the cup I thought, 'At last my dream has come true.'

MICHAEL WARREN, ST OLIVER PLUNKETT NS, KILKERRIN, BALLINASLOE, COUNTY GALWAY

I have a dream of a moonlit beach
That sits so solemn and still.
Nobody thinks and nobody cares
Of a beach so solemn and still.

On that beach so solemn and still
The grass grows across the white sands,
And on the seabed, where the sharks do roam
A shipwreck, ghostly, still stands.

And in the great sky the stars can be seen,
The galaxies are all there.
And down to the east lies a crescent moon,
And it hangs so still in the air.

At the foot of the cliff the sea is still
And there isn't a ripple in sight.
In the rock pools no fish can be seen,
They've all gone in for the night.

I have a dream of a moonlit beach
That sits so solemn and still.
Nobody thinks and nobody cares
Of a beach so solemn and still.

AOIFE FITZGERALD (8), CONVENT NS,
CAPPAMORE, COUNTY LIMERICK

I have a dream that some day I will compete in the
Olympic Games and represent my country, Ireland. I
have a dream of beating the top athletes in the world.
Some time in the future, Ireland will host the Olympic
Games. I have a dream that I will be standing on the
winners' stand on the top step, bending my head
forward to receive a gold medal and be presented with
a bouquet of flowers.

I dream of setting a new Olympic record in the 1,000
metres race – the fastest time for the next millennium –
and proudly listening to my national anthem being
played.

I do hope my dream comes true.

SHANE REYNOLDS (11), ABBEYCARTRON NS,
ELPHIN, COUNTY ROSCOMMON

I have a dream
A dream, yeah right,
Nightmare's my thing –
Rotting eyeballs, scary sights.
Headless horsemen,
You'd be in for a scare,
Running round through the night,
You'd want to beware.

But most of all,
In the back of my mind.
Terrifying sights
Of all different kinds.

Though at eight o'clock
When I get out of bed,
Horsemen and eyeballs –
It's all in my head.

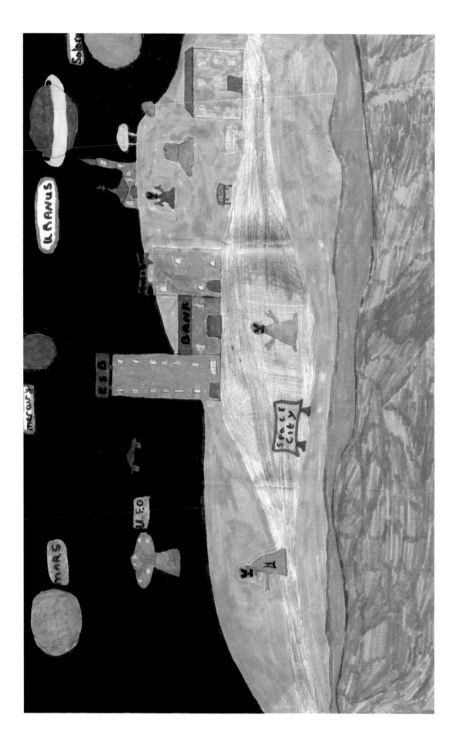

KEVIN GUILLY, 10 ARD MHUIRE, UPPER AGHADA, MIDLETON, CO CORK

I have a dream that I am a dog and I wander off into the woods and get lost. I go deeper into the woods. I meet a squirrel. She says I should go home because it is getting late – it's teatime. I don't want to go home so I go off to find a place to sleep. I ask the mouse, the snakes, the squirrels, the owls, the badgers, the foxes, the wolves and the deer. Then I come to the bat. She lets me sleep in her cosy cave. When it is morning she brings me hunting. I get lovely things to eat. Then she brings me for a walk. And would you believe it, she brings me home. The children that own me run out and pick me up in their arms. The mammy and daddy come out and we have a big party and the bat shares it with us.

'I have a dream' – at last he spoke –
'yet still reality roams on.
I look past a distant month,
Son, why is my dream gone?

'I see a hope, I see a light,
as a night strikes on,
I look past another week,
Son, why is my hope gone?

Soon another day is born
As the dawn creeps on,
I look past a distant day,
Son, why is this day gone?'

His last words echo through my head
As I wander off to bed,
I hear these words during the night,
I see a hope, I see a light,

And in the mist of a new morn
I dream – another day is born.

In the echoes of my mind,
While the day wears on,
The hardest question I can find –
'Son, why is my dream gone?'

I dreamt a dying dream of peace;
I have a question too:
Since it is now a dead dream,
Is it because of you?

CHRISTINA RYAN (8), DOON CONVENT NS, COUNTY LIMERICK

I have a dream
Almost every night –
But some of them
Make me jump with fright –

Of beetles and bugs,
Crawlies and slugs,
Oh how I hate them,
Somebody wake me up!

Oh no, they're coming towards me,
A black beetle has spotted my toe,
I scream and scream and scream
For this horrible dream to go.

First he winks, then he waves.
He smiles at me
And wanders off to play
I hope this time he'll stay away.

MARLIN NÍ DHÓNAILL (9), SCOIL NÁISIÚNTA ARAINN MHOR 2,
LEITIR CEANAINN, CONTAE DHUN NA NGALL

My dream is to see my brother again. My dream is that he is still alive. If he were alive I would be a good sister to him and he would be a good brother to me. When he died I was not alive. He got knocked down by a tractor. He was one and a half. When my Mum told me I started to cry. His name was Patrick. If I saw him I would be happy. When I die I will meet him and my Grandad. If he was still alive I would play with him and he would play with me and we would go to the shops together. My dream is to say hello to my brother.

LOUISE GLANCY (8), AUGHRIM NS,
CARRICK-ON-SHANNON, COUNTY LEITRIM

I have a dream – I'd love to be
A cute little rabbit under a tree,
With bushy tail and ears that flop
And four strong legs that help me hop.

59

I'd hop around from dawn till dusk,
I'd dig a burrow deep in the dust,
I'd care all day for my family
And fetch their food till they can see.

Then out in the sun we'd spend the day,
With all our friends who'd come to play.
The mice and squirrels are very dear,
But foxes and weasels we always fear.

We'd feed on grass and lettuce green,
Then wash our whiskers in the stream.
We'd play on the sand and chew at logs,
And still watch out for men with dogs.

I hear my mother calling me,
I look around to find the tree,
No more rabbits do I see.
'Louise, wake up! It's time for tea.'

LEAH WALDRON (11), ST ORAN'S NS, COCKHILL,
BUNCRANA, COUNTY DONEGAL

I have a dream to tell to you,
About a world, a world so new.
I have a dream, where I can see
A wonderful place for you and me.

In my dream, all wars are ended,
All hate is gone, all fights are mended.
There is plenty of food to feed the poor,
It's a wonderful, wonderful world for sure.

There are no earthquakes, floods or fire
And everyone gets what they desire.
People everywhere can see
This world's a really good place to be.

There's no pollution in my dream,
The rivers run clear, all grass is green,
Animals are treated with kindness and care
And people all over are good and fair.

People will remember to thank God above
For our lives, and all his love.
In my dream, my dream comes true,
It's a wonderful world for me and you.

I walk into the mist. I keep walking and I enter Giant World.

I find myself on a giant black rabbit. The rabbit's called Harry. He is eating grass and I am eating nuts. A big blue monster with sharp teeth suddenly appears and laughs fiercely.

I get on Harry's back and we gallop to our hole. The monster is chasing us. We dig down and down and we surprisingly enter a mole's party. We are invited in. All around us is bell music and we enjoy mole-cake. We each receive a fantastic present.

Slowly, like a painting, everything drips, drips away. Suddenly I am in the mist and I walk sadly back to my class.

FEARGHAL MCANESPY (11), ST JOSEPH'S PRIMARY SCHOOL,
LISCONREA, FINTONA, COUNTY TYRONE

I have a dream
of peace,

of a world
where
there are no killings,

where
children can go to school with no worry of a visit
from
a gun-toting madman,

where
you can see a bunch of teenagers
and feel safe,

where
different religions can agree – to differ,

where
we don't have to worry about watching the news,

where
there are no back-alley punishment shootings,

where
there are no petrol-bomb attacks,

and where
TYRONE win SAM!

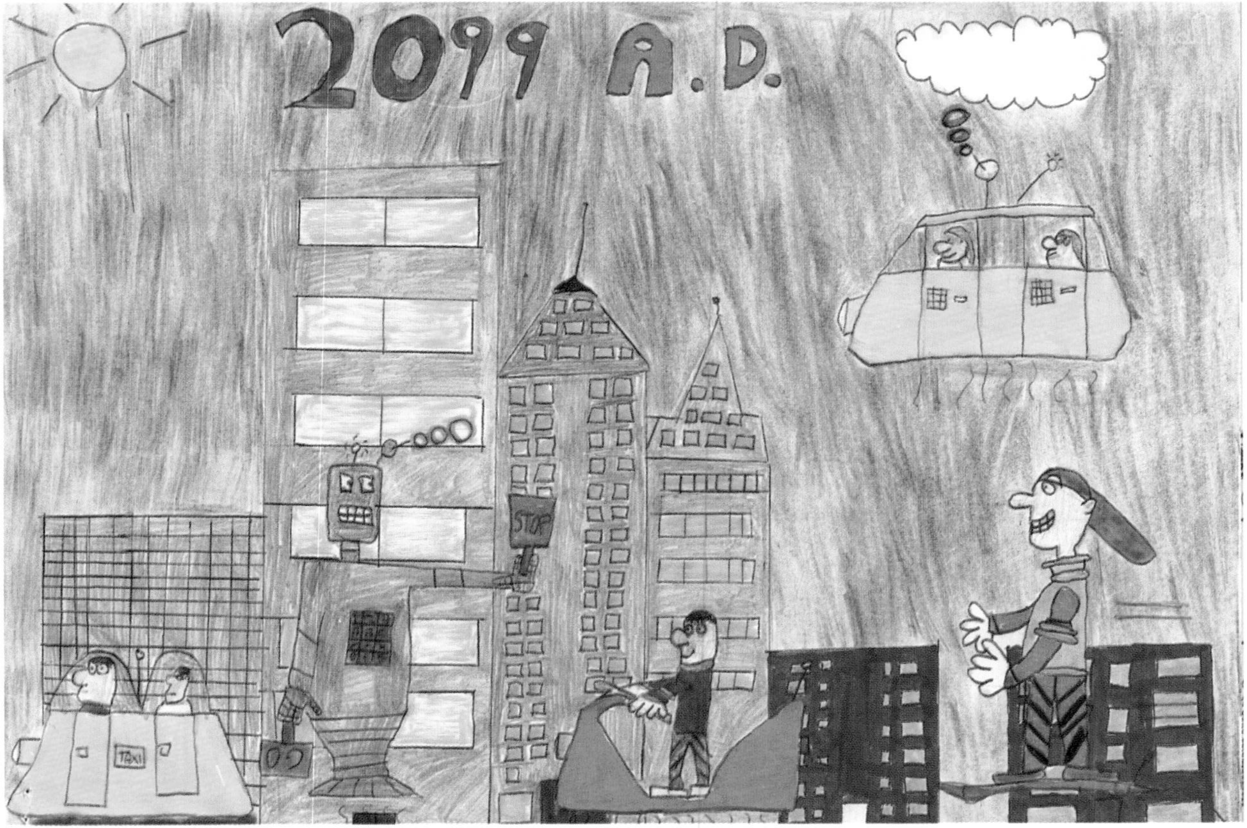

Allan Mee, St Joseph's NS, Kilfinane, Co Limerick

SARAH EGAN (9), OUR LADY OF LOURDES NS,
BALLINLOUGH, CORK

I have a dream that I could fly,
That I could swoop up and down
Like a golden eagle,
That I would watch the evening sunset up on a roof.
I would be safe, magnificent,
But most of all graceful.
I would give everything up for wings,
Even for one day, one hour, one minute.
To be a bird must be wonderful,
For to them, there's no such thing as gravity.
I would not waste a second of my time
If I could just fly.
Oh, to feel the wind rushing through my hair,
The breeze against my skin,
The world within my grasp.
All so new and free.
So many things to discover,
So many things to explore.
Oh, to fly.
Oh, the joy of it all.

MAEVE SIMONS, COOLNASMEAR NS, DUNGARVAN,
COUNTY WATERFORD

I have a dream
That as new dawn breaks
The shadows of hate
Shall fade away,

The pools of jealousy
Shall dry up,
The streams of evil
Shall run no more.

I have a dream
That as a new sun sets
The rain of good
Shall feed the earth,

The river of generosity
Shall spill from its banks
And the ocean of love
Shall unite the world.

I fell asleep and when I woke my room looked different. The walls were grey and there was one candle on a shelf in the corner of the room. I walked down the creepy stairs and in the next room there was a small kitchen. The floors were cold and grey. There were pots and pans hanging up and a small table in the corner with cheese and stale bread. Then I heard somebody calling my name. I ran outside to see who was there. I saw an old lady in very old-fashioned clothes. She said, 'You have a lot of work to do.' She told me to milk the cows and collect the eggs from the barn. I thought that I had seen a ghost. I worked very hard and was exhausted when I had finished. It was all so strange that I ran upstairs and began to cry. I must have fallen fast asleep because when I woke up, my room had returned to normal. I ran downstairs and was very happy to see my family sitting at the table having their breakfast. Just then the toast popped out of the toaster and the telephone rang. I think that things were very different 150 years ago. Don't you?

SARAH P. DOYLE (9), ST MARGARET'S NS, COUNTY DUBLIN

I have a dream,
My very own time machine,
Travelling back,
Being on the scene,
The Pharaohs, the cavemen, dinosaurs too,
All those I would see
When they were brand new.
To be in the stable where Jesus was born,
Oh, to be there that first Christmas morn.
To thank the inventors of
Chocolate, TV, toys and the phone,
Gameboys, the Playstation, the '99' cone.
To travel forward
My future to see.
I hope it works out
Really good for me.

ALICE MCKEON (8), STONEPARK NS, COUNTY LONGFORD

I have a dream. I love horses and I would love to have a pony of my own, but Mammy and Daddy say that there are other things I need more. My big sister says the new millennium is coming and all sorts of magic can happen.

Suddenly I am in the sitting room. It is New Year's Eve. The fire is burning brightly and the snow is falling outside. I am feeling very sleepy. My sisters are asking me to go for a walk. We all get torches. Our feet make a crunching noise. The snow is beautiful. The sky is turning dark blue – soon it will be pitch black. The stars are twinkling. The round bales look strange covered with snow.

We are walking slowly. My feet are getting heavy. My sisters are chatting to each other. One wants to travel – the other one wants to go to college. I am falling behind them but they don't seem to notice. I hear a noise in the bushes. The trees wave back and forth and the wind is getting louder. I can still hear the noise. It sounds like footsteps. The snow is falling heavier. It's hard to see. I am frightened.

A horse is coming towards me. He is white. As white as the snow. I am up on his back now. I can't see my sisters anymore. There's just me and my horse. We seem to be going home. It's a great feeling up here on his back. What will I call him – 'Snowflake', maybe?

I hear Mammy calling me. She sounds far away. I wonder what she will think of my horse?

I have a dream
But before I tell you my plan
Try and guess it if you can.
Is my dream to sail a big ship
Around the world on a very long trip?
Is my dream to be an actress on stage
Learning my lines page after page?
Is my dream to climb a mountain high
Till I can almost touch the sky?
Is my dream to go to the moon
To see if there's a giant monster with a big spoon?
Is my dream to own a million cats
And travel the world killing all the rats?
Or is my dream to sculpture sand?
No
I have a dream.
My dream is to be
First woman Taoiseach of Ireland.

RICHARD CARNEY, ABBEYCARTRON NS, ELPHIN, CO ROSCOMMON

ÁINE NÍ CHONAILL, SCOIL AONGHUSA,

DROICHEAD ÁTHA, CONTAE LÚ

I have a dream to own a pony,
All I need to do is save some money.
I'd love to ride him every day
And rub his mane and feed him hay.
I'd love to gallop over hills and dales
And feel the wind and hear the gales.
I'd call my pony Lucky Ted,
I'd keep him safe inside his shed
When winter comes and there's wind and snow
And temperatures are well below.
But in summer – that's my favourite season –
We'd play and swim and run about,
We'd have great fun without a doubt.
I have a dream to own a pony
With a chestnut coat and a tail that's bony,
Blue eyes, pink nose, a mischievous smile.
Well, that's my dream – I'm off to sleep for a while.

SHARON BEIRNE (8), ABBEYCARTRON NS,
ELPHIN, COUNTY ROSCOMMON

I have a dream
The clouds are cream
The earth is full of chocolate
The rain is made from lemonade
And I whiz to school in a zooming rocket.

The stars that shine up very high
Are magic twinkles in the sky
And every tree grows Maltesers free
In my wonderful dream world.

There's a talking bee on *Den TV*
And the coolest donkey you ever would see
And a flying bear with ketchup in his hair
Reads the six o'clock news on RTÉ.

'I have a dream' are the words spoken by Martin Luther King to tell the world that he had a hope that black people could be friends with white people. Dr King was a brave man to tell the world about his dream because people can laugh at you and say it will never happen, but my Dad says that if you have a dream you can make it come true if you want it badly enough. I have a dream that I will swim for my country. Some people might not think I will do it but I have already started to work to make my dreams come true. Last March I met a man who helped me believe I can make my dream come true. His name is John Olson. John Olson is an American Olympic medal winner. He has won five gold medals. John told me that when he was going to school nobody believed he would swim in the Olympics, but he did, because he was prepared to work hard to make his dream come true. When he showed me one of his gold medals and let me hold it, I knew it was what I wanted. I could see myself standing on the podium and the announcer saying, 'Ladies and gentlemen, please stand for the Irish national anthem', and I would see my flag being raised.

This is my dream.

I have a dream of things to come,
Will they be gloomy or will they be fun?

I have a dream of peace some day,
Will it be now, or another day?

I have a dream of winning the Lotto,
It might be today, if not, tomorrow.

Our country is in a bit of a state,
I have a dream that it's too late.

I have a dream I will grow up some day
To be big and strong and helpful in every way.

I have a dream when I go to bed
And when I wake up it's gone from my head.

I have a dream when I'm watching *Den 2*
That in the millennium I'll be there with you.

AMY QUINN (9), MOTHER OF DIVINE GRACE SCHOOL,
FINGLAS EAST, DUBLIN

I have a dream, to dream of things that will never
come true,
A dream is a world I never knew,
A dream itself is precious to me,
For it's a world only I can see.
Believe me, for I have seen,
Whatever you do, don't waste a dream.

MICHAEL DANIEL COSTELLO (8), COLÁISTE PHÁDRAIG BOYS' NS,
DRUMCONDRA, DUBLIN

I have a dream this world could be
A place where children could be free –
Free from hunger, free from pain,
Free from wars, where rich men gain,
Where children suffer, people die –
Where grown-ups can rule countries
Without bombs and guns and fights,
No burning flames or children maimed,
Fleeing to the mountains and the hills at night.

Where children could be presidents
And rulers of the nation,
Then the leaders, kings and ministers
Could master Sega and Playstation.

The kids would make computer games
To teach the grown-ups how it's done.
They'd share out all the nation's wealth
And give it to the countries that have none.

They'd have a Disneyland in every town,
A McDonald's in every school,
Robots to do the homework –
Who says kids ain't cool?

Superheroes could be teachers –
You can just hear the grown-ups sigh –
Superman and Spiderman could
Teach the kids to fly.

People wouldn't have to sleep
In doorways on the street –
A little place they could call home,
Maybe even enough to eat.

Dustin could help out here
With his bit of two-be-four.
He's a builder and a mate of mine –
Last week he fixed me door.

I have a dream for the millennium,
Violence and injustice it could cease,
People learn to love and share,
My dream – a world where there is peace.

ANDREW FINN (9), TAUGHEEN NS,
CLAREMORRIS, COUNTY MAYO

My dream is for peace all over the world. Will this thought always be a dream or will it become reality?
The first place I visit in my dream is my own country, Ireland. Such a small country, yet divided in two by mindless violence. Even in a time of so-called peace we had to witness the brutal killings of the Omagh bombing. Even in a dream I cannot find a reason for it.

Next I journey across Europe to Bosnia, another small country, where again I witness the slaughter of thousands of innocent people. Can this be a dream? From here I journey to East Timor. Again we have the same story – innocent people are dying for no reason. In my dream I have travelled across the world, seeing small countries torn apart by war.

As I start my homeward journey I begin to see changes passing over all the same places. The difference on this journey is that, as I pass over these countries, I see people laughing and smiling, people of all races playing and working together. There are no guns, no bombs, no diseases and no borders dividing us.

Then I awake safe and secure in my own bed, and I start to cry. I say out loud, 'I have a dream.'

SHARON BEIRNE, ABBEYCARTRON NS, ELPHIN, CO ROSCOMMON

ERIN BARCLAY (8), CORONEA, SKIBBEREEN, COUNTY CORK

I have a dream to own a pony,
At night I close my eyes and wish, 'If only, if only.'
I would ride her and talk to her every day,
I'd feed her and groom her and pet her and play.

We don't have a horsebox, a field or a stable,
I could build a shelter if only I was able.
Dad can't help me, he has a bad back,
And another thing – we don't have the tack.

Last week at full moon we had a fairy ring,
I watched it at midnight and hoped to hear them sing.
I've heard if that happens your wish will come true.
They helped me once before, a secret I can't tell you.

I have a dream to own a pony,
At night I close my eyes and wish, 'If only, if only.'
I would do anything, I'd give it a whack,
If I get what I want I'll be away in a hack.

FIONA GILLON (9), CLYDAGH NS,
HEADFORD, COUNTY GALWAY

I have a dream,
It might come true,
I really, really
Want it to!

I wish I could
Be on TV
And everyone
Would watch and see.

I wish I could be
On *Den 2*
Or I'd like to be
On *Scooby-doo*!

I'd like to be on
Ship to Shore,
And I'd love to be
On lots, lots more!

I have a dream,
It might come true,
I really, really
Want it to!

I have a dream that I could go back 650 million years ago to when dinosaurs lived on the earth. The dinosaurs would not be ferocious but very friendly and I could ride on a triceratops' back. I would be able to see a Tyrannosaurus Rex and maybe fly up to the sky on a pteranodon. I would be able to warn them about the meteor that was coming, and then dinosaurs would still be around today.

STEPHANIE FLEMING (11), SCOIL BHRÍDE,
EGLANTINE PARK, CORK

I have a dream
A new millennium
A different day
Where war is gone
and children play
In places where
a war was on
but now there's peace and sanctuary
Where good prevails with
evil begging on its knees
For a childhood dream of peace

Nowadays is far too common
Not a trace of war
Guns are no more
Than a relic within a glass
case in a museum
Houses built in places
Long ago distraught
Peace is as common
as a human thought
Liberation a common thing
Whereas now it's as
common as a
pig with wings
Human race come to your senses
For when this happens peace commences

ADRIAN GILLIGAN, CRAUGHWELL NS, COUNTY GALWAY

I have a dream that I am face to face with an animal. But not any ordinary animal. He has a snake's head and a horse's tail and five stripes from a tiger. He runs after me around the whole jungle to catch me. He never catches me because I wake up. Once he nearly caught me but I moved out of the way and then he died and I never saw him again. So if you see him in real life, I suppose you should move out of his way.

ENDA DORRIAN, ST JOHN'S NS, SLIGO

I have a dream that just one night
I'll see the stars shining bright,
Right up close in the sky,
In my spaceship flying by.

I have a dream that I will be
An Irish astronaut, you see.
I'll fly my ship to the planet Venus
And maybe I'll become very famous.

Maybe I'll see an alien ten feet tall,
With great big eyes but no teeth at all.
I'd bring him home to earth with me,
He'd be my friend in my country.

SEÁN Ó LAIGHIN, SCOIL MOLÓGA, BÓTHAR CHARLEVILLE, CROS ARAILD, BAILE ÁTHA CLIATH

I have a dream of being on a team.
I have a dream of Will Smith being a myth.
I have a dream of time to climb.
I have a dream of frogs being dogs.
I have a dream of stars being cars.
I have a dream of books being crooks.
I have a dream of bees being trees.
I have a dream of Hercules being Gercules.
I have a dream of school being cool.
I have a dream of television being a relevision.

GERALDINE IRWIN (9), ST TERESA'S PRIMARY SCHOOL, BELFAST

One night when I was sleeping I heard an unusual knock on my very creaky door. I said softly, so that I wouldn't wake anyone, 'Stop fooling around.' I looked at my watch and it was totally blank, so I decided to go out and turn the light on. Slowly and cautiously I opened the door and I couldn't believe my eyes. I couldn't even move, as I was in shock. For I found myself no longer in my room but in a strange-looking forest.

The forest had lovely brown trees and these were not

blocking even a single ray of light. The grass, as smooth as fur, wound down an everlasting trail. Little animals were scampering everywhere in all directions. The little lovebirds were singing happily. The forest was so pretty. I began to explore this wonderful place when all the baby animals began to crowd around me, trying to tell me something. I knelt down to see what they wanted. I couldn't understand them so I tried to walk a little bit further but they ran in front of me to try and stop me from leaving. Suddenly a giant owl came and said wisely, 'Hey there, my little animal friends are trying to tell you not to go any further because there are very fierce giants over the hill with very dangerous weapons and they would like it very much if they could catch you.' The owl could see there was fear in my eyes, so he continued, 'May I introduce you to the magic forest – a place of wonder and imagination. If only we could rid ourselves of the dreaded giants.'

Once I had got my breath back I said, 'I'll go to see if I can stop these terrible monsters', but the owl warned me once more to be very careful. So off I went down the hill and there at the bottom were the most enormous giants. I tried to hide but a giant spotted me and came charging towards me. He swung his club at me and I crouched low so he couldn't hit me. Just then all the nice animals came running like lightning, as if they were trying to protect me. The owl shouted, 'Run to the nearest door.' So off I went running down the steep hill, dodging the other giants. I saw a big, old house (nearly as tall as a castle!), and I opened its enormous brown door. I didn't dare to look behind me. I shut the door, which made a big 'bang!' The room was unbearable. I was like a mouse compared to the house. It was awfully quiet. I tried to listen to hear noises but there were none. I sniffed, and something smelt rotten. I wondered what it was. I saw another door opposite me. I walked towards it and heard a noise getting louder. I was scared to death. I said to myself, 'I have to open it.' So I opened it, and the next thing I knew I was safe in my own house. My brothers were trying to wake me. What a night. I was even more tired when I woke up!

Jane Holton (7), Ballinakill, Longwood,
Enfield, County Meath

I have a dream of things to come,
Of eclipses, space parties and nice easy sums.
I see school lasting one hour and lunchtime three,
And a spaceship to pick up my sister and me.

And when I grow up I'll farm with my Dad,
We'll have robots to do all the work on the land.
I'll fly, when I want, to Venus or Mars,
And we'll all drive spaceships instead of cars.

LAUREN FEGAN, ST ANTHONY'S PRIMARY SCHOOL, BELFAST

I have a dream that on millennium eve, the millennium
bug will spread to my house and affect us all in strange
ways.
  'Ten, nine, eight, seven, six, five, four, three, two, one,
HAPPY NEW MILLEN . . .
  What the . . . ?'
  Dustin's trying to sing to us from the microwave,
  The TV's going 'Bing! Bing!',
  The oven's keeping the milk nice and fresh,
  The turkey is cooking nicely in the fridge.
  The computer is dealing real solitaire cards at me,
  The dishwasher is drying the clothes,
  The steam iron is spitting out ice cubes all over the
kitchen,
  There's a plane coming to land in the back garden!
  Just when I think the worst is over
  The burglar alarm goes off.
  The hall door is flung open by my hysterical mother,
  Screaming, 'I'm a millionaire!
  And I only wanted ten pounds from the bank
machine.'
  The hoover is chasing my dog around the house
  With my granny attached to the nozzle,
  Shouting, 'The bugs were easier to control in my day.'

What a millennium party it will be,
If my house comes alive with millennium fever!
I also wonder if millennium dreams really can come true.
Well, we'll have to wait and see!

DANIELA CARDILLO, THE KILKENNY SCHOOL PROJECT,
SPRINGFIELDS, KILKENNY

I have a dream to live by the sea and own my own stud farm. I'd breed big and small strong-willed Connemaras that would be known for their good hearts. I'd breed elegant Andalusians, with their long flowing manes and tails and glossy coats. I'd also breed little Welsh ponies that would frolic around playfully in the fields and many, many more beautiful breeds. I would have a pure black Andalusian stallion called Furio. People would come from miles around for him to cover their mares. I'd go trekking on the beaches, galloping up and down. I'd go bareback into the water to let my horse cool down. I would own brilliant showing and dressage horses and win lots of events. In the evening we would go for walks in the pine forest overlooking the big blue ocean. There would be a strong smell of pine as we walked along the forest. It would be calm and soothing. As we headed home we would stop at the clifftop to watch the sun setting on the horizon. The sky would be pink and orange. It would look like a fire growing dimmer and dimmer. When it would finally go down, we would start to walk home. As I untack my horse I'd still be able to smell the pine strongly. I'd live in a red-brick house. The grounds would have hundreds of acres for my horses and ponies. The stables would be lined up beside each other. The wooden doorstop would be open so the horses could see out. I would have two indoor and two outdoor arenas. My friends would live in the house with me. They would keep their horses in my stables. My stables would be called 'ar nos na gaoithe'. I would also have a cat and a dog. I would make all my money out of Furio. After checking all the horses, I'd go in for a rest myself. I'd lay my head down on the pillow to go to sleep. I would hear the waves bashing off the cliff face. I dream of this dream coming true.

SARAH O'NEILL (7), ST PATRICK'S PRIMARY SCHOOL,
DUNGANNON, COUNTY TYRONE

Make the environment clean and healthy to live in.
If people are sick make them better.
Let there be cures for all the bad diseases like cancer.
Let all the bad people get taken away and put

together so that they cannot harm little children.

Everybody in Northern Ireland could live in peace and stop violence.

Nobody would be homeless or poor.

If any home had no computer it would get one.

Use computers to help people in other countries.

My mummy and all the other mummies in the world would get £2,000 because it is the year 2000.

MAIRÉAD MOLLOY, KILLOCRAUN NS, CASTLEHILL, BALLINA, COUNTY MAYO

I have a dream that I could walk like my brother and sisters. My condition does not affect my school work. I look at my friends at school run and walk. Being in a wheelchair slows me down but I don't mind. When I go to Dublin I go by train. Someone has to help me change trains. The step is too high for me. It is hard to take my wheelchair out of the train. My teacher is very good to me. She understands when I say I would like to walk. I can do things that my friends cannot do, like wheelies, wheelchair racing and other things.

In the future I will be independent, DV. I will be able to go to Mass, the shops and on and off trains. I hope to have a house with ramps going in and out. I have no problem moving around in my wheelchair.

DEVON CONWAY, BRUSNA NS,
BALLAGHADERREEN, COUNTY ROSCOMMON

I have a dream that I was on a lovely star.
It was a very bright star.
It was a very playful star.
It was not lonely.
It was a very loving star.

When it was going I started to cry because I was not
lonely before
And he was my only friend.
He was giddy sometimes and very jumpy and very
nice and very funny.
I was happy all the time and when I was sad he could
make me happy.
And when he was sad I could make him happy.
He was my favourite friend.

RÓISÍN CARRUTHERS, GAELSCOIL AN EISCIR RIADA,
TULACH MÓR, CONTAE UÍBH FHÁILÍ

I have a dream . . . sort of a weird one! I'd like it if, in
the future, humans could communicate with animal
life. I think it would be very interesting if we could
have conversations with dogs, to see if they really love

us, or to ask birds, 'What's flying like?' Maybe chimps could tell us some more information, to find out are we really their cousins? How about striking a deal with snakes: we won't use your skin if you don't poison us! However, I don't think we'd get many compliments from pigs and cows. Or maybe they don't know their fate? We could ask! It would be fun to have a chat with your pet. I think I'll try and make my dream come true when I grow up. I'll try! In the meantime, it's just my dream, but someday (hopefully) I can argue with an elephant!

ANDREW KELLY, DRUMGOSSATT NS,
CARRICKMACROSS, COUNTY MONAGHAN

I have a dream every night
About a dog and a cat and a rat on a mat.
And the cat eats the rat and the dog eats the cat,
And lies on the mat.
And chokes on the cat.